Endless Beginning

オートモアイ

I'M NOT
HUMAN

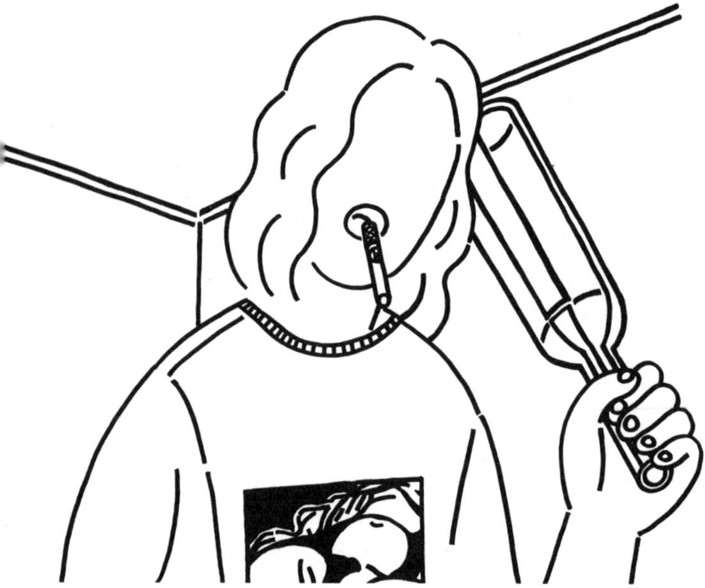

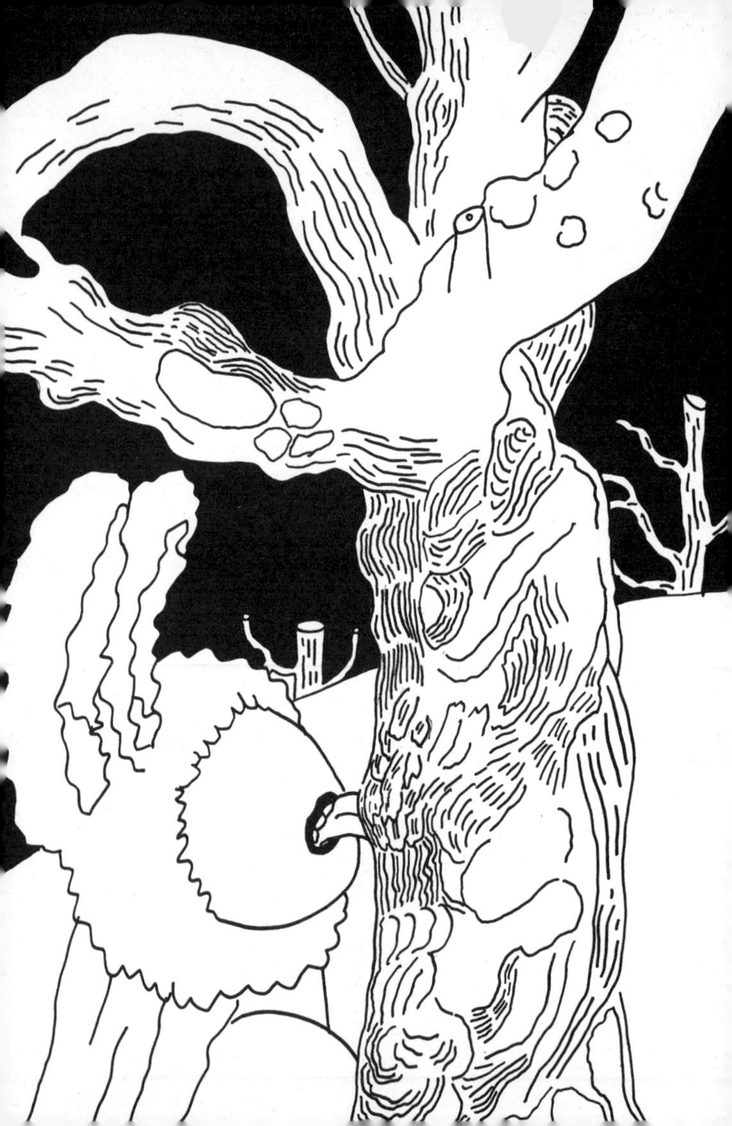

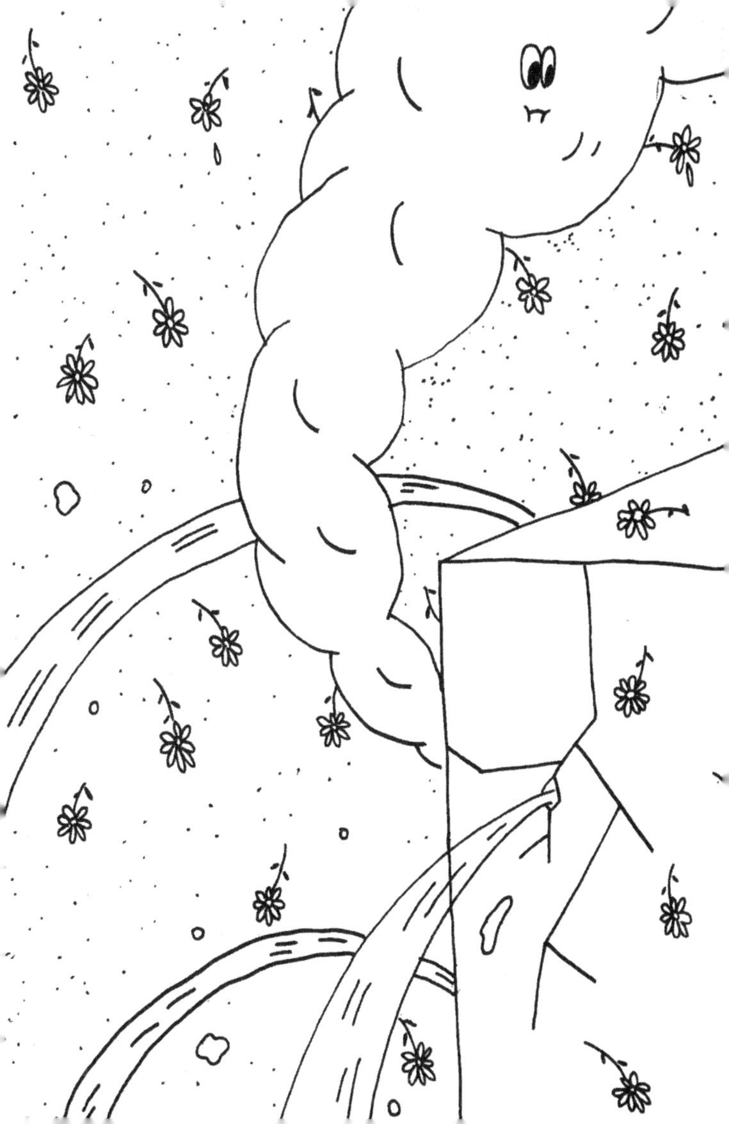

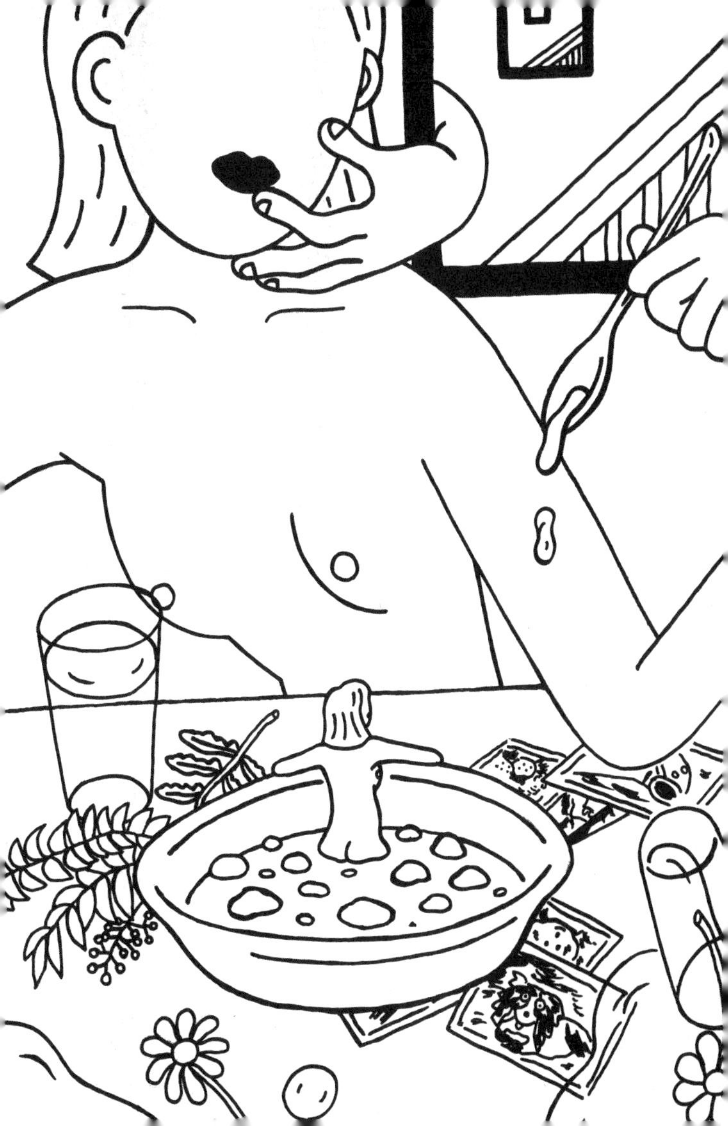

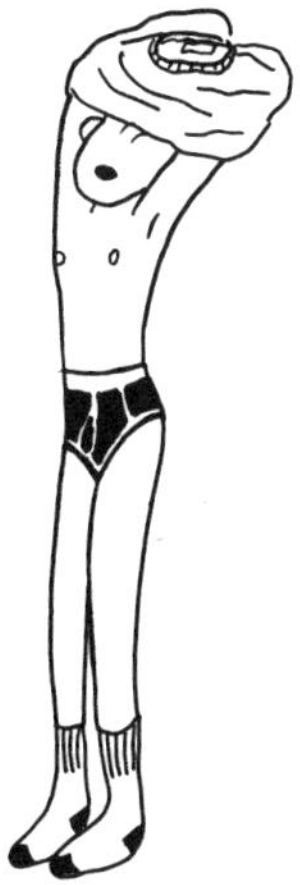

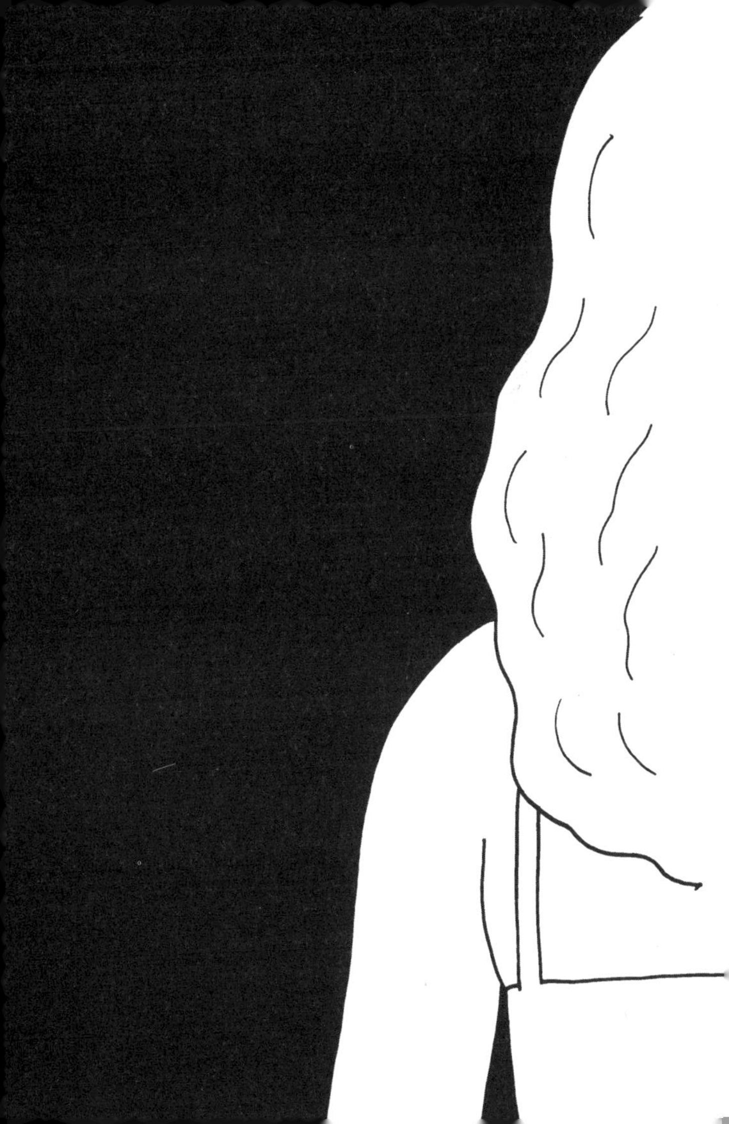

FILTERS

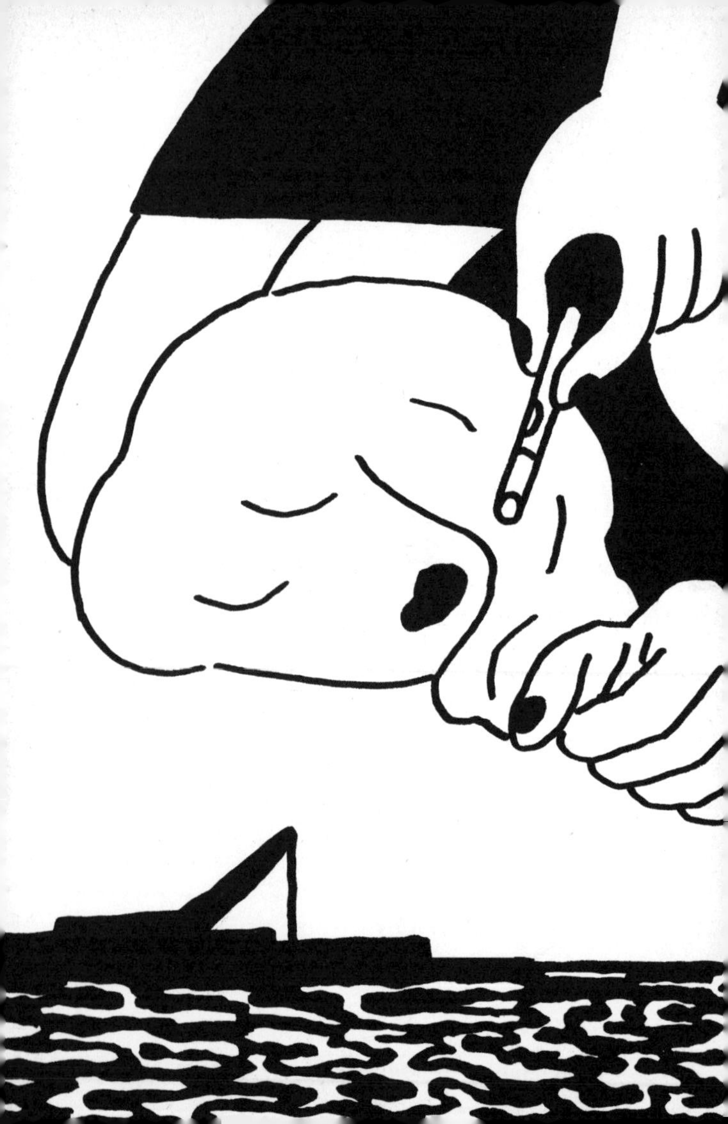

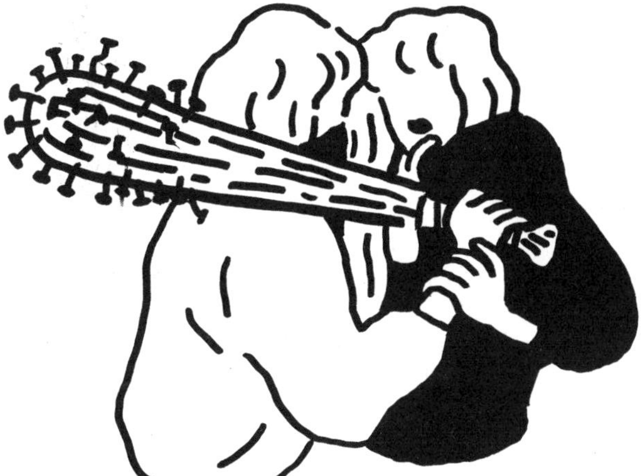

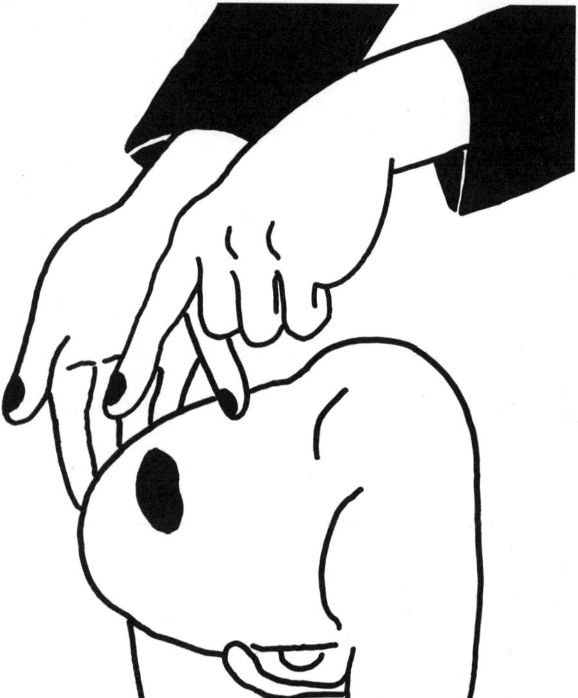

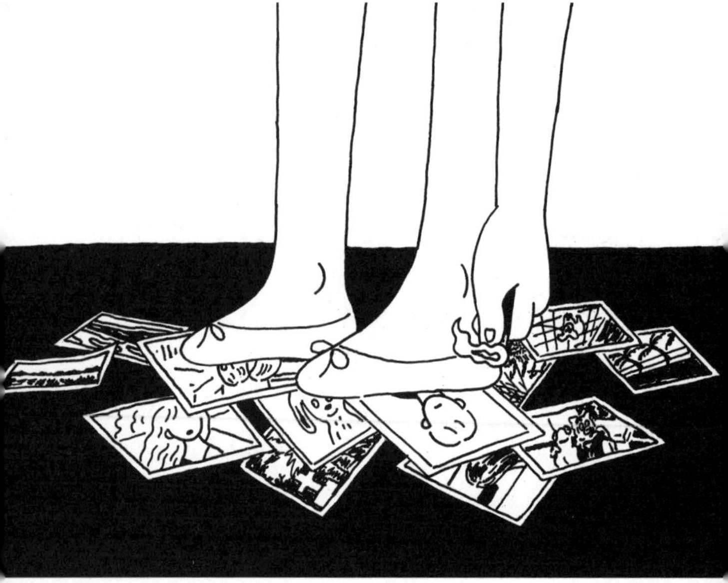

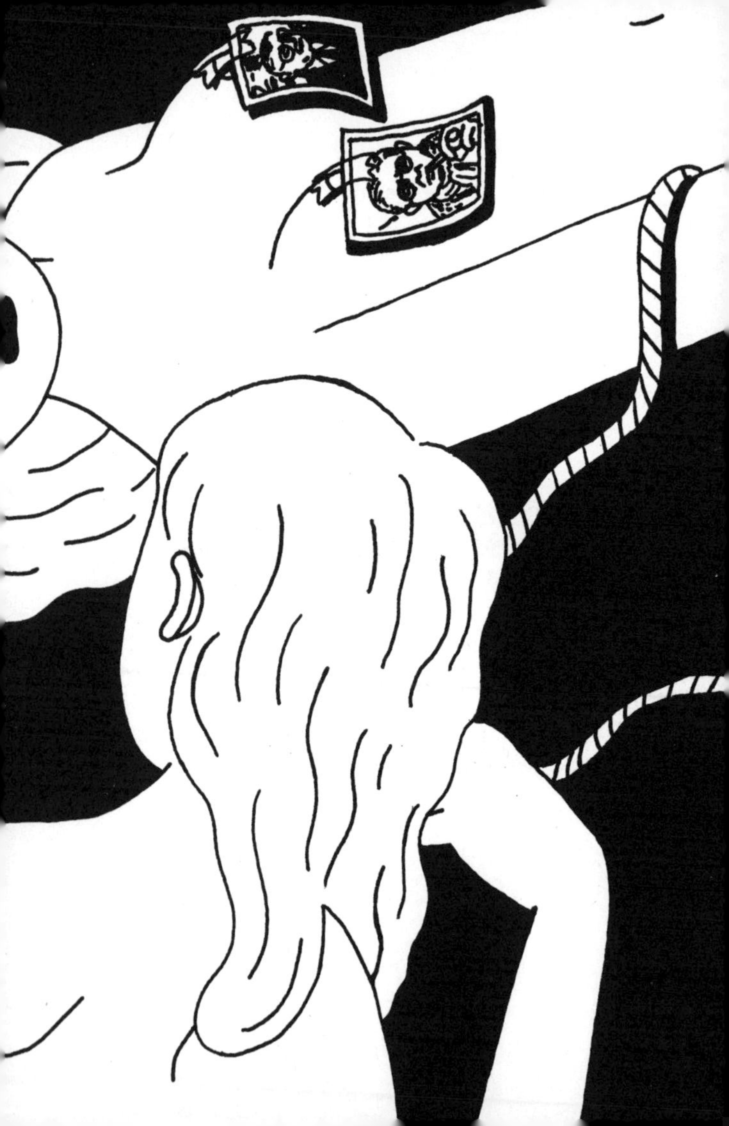

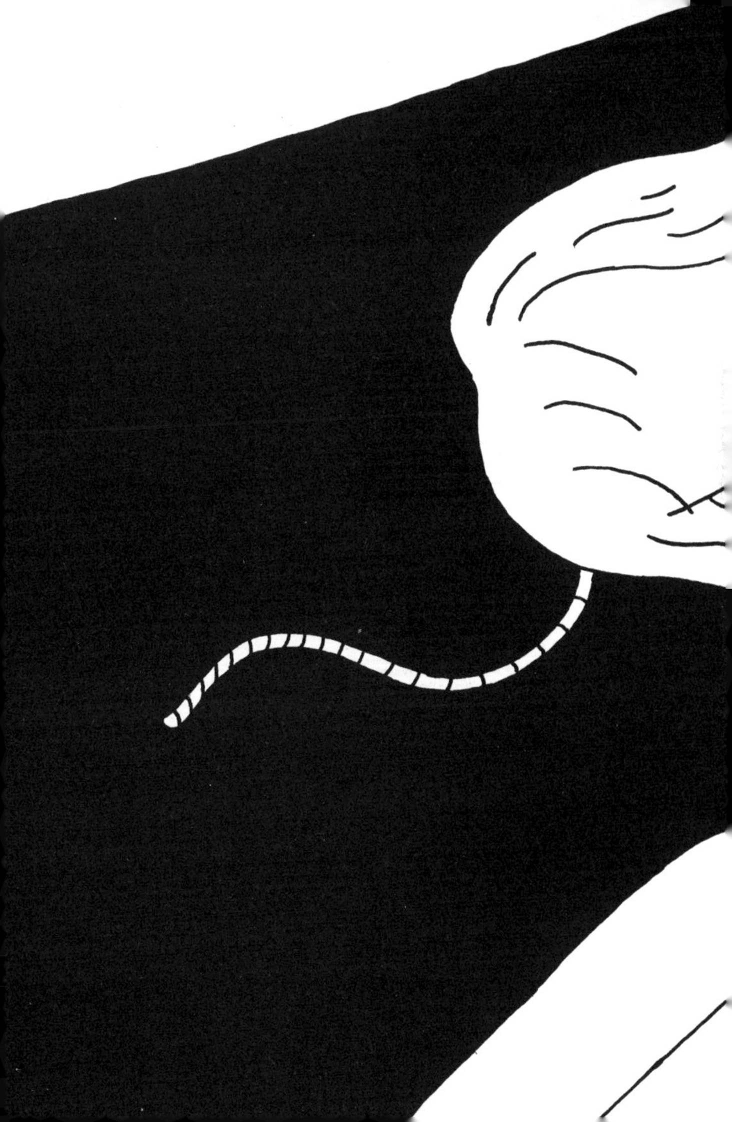

Ginza
OPE

AUTOMOAI
solo
Exhibition
2015
3.7 Sun-3.11 Wed

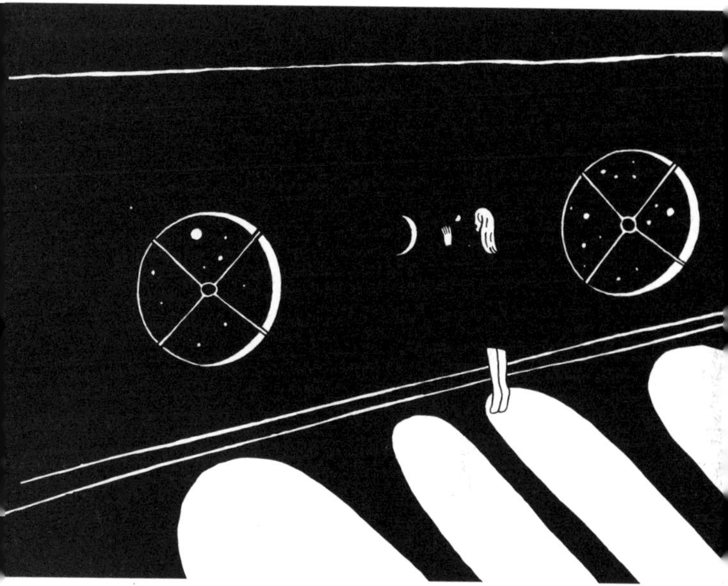

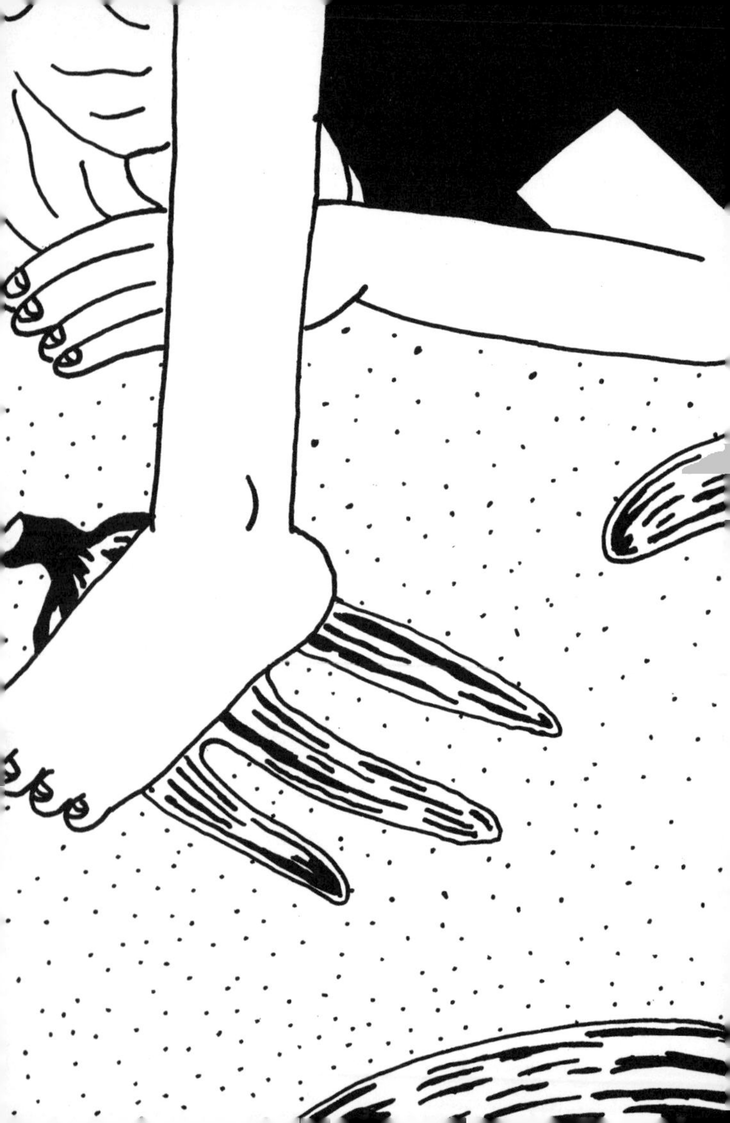

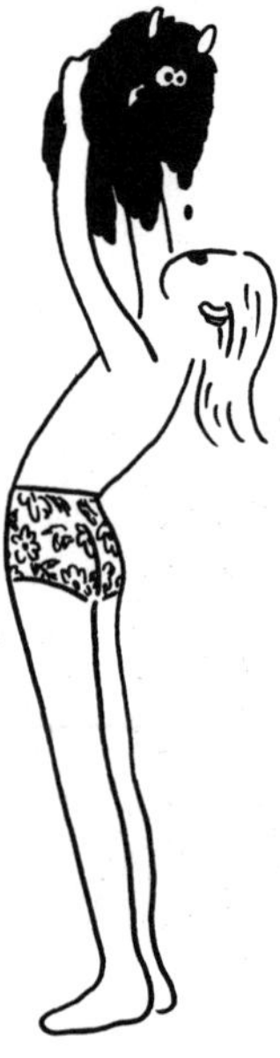

F

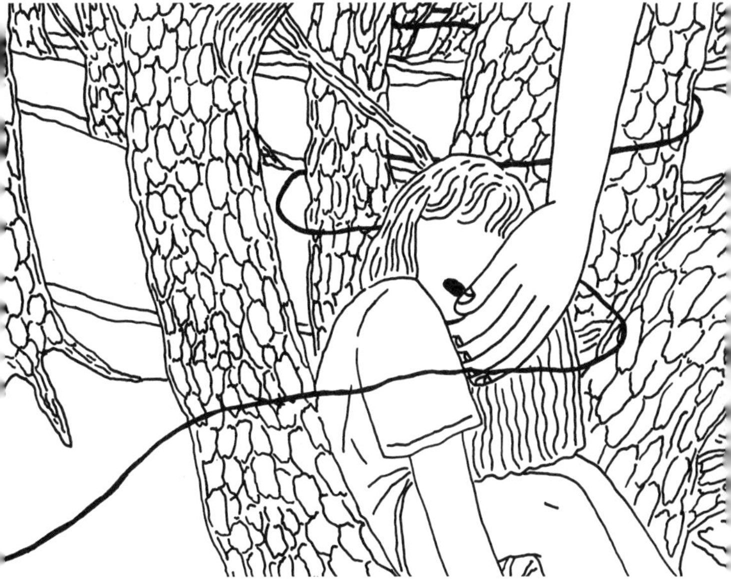

bit hit gone to shit as well
SWITCHBLADE SISTERS

Burnable Garbage

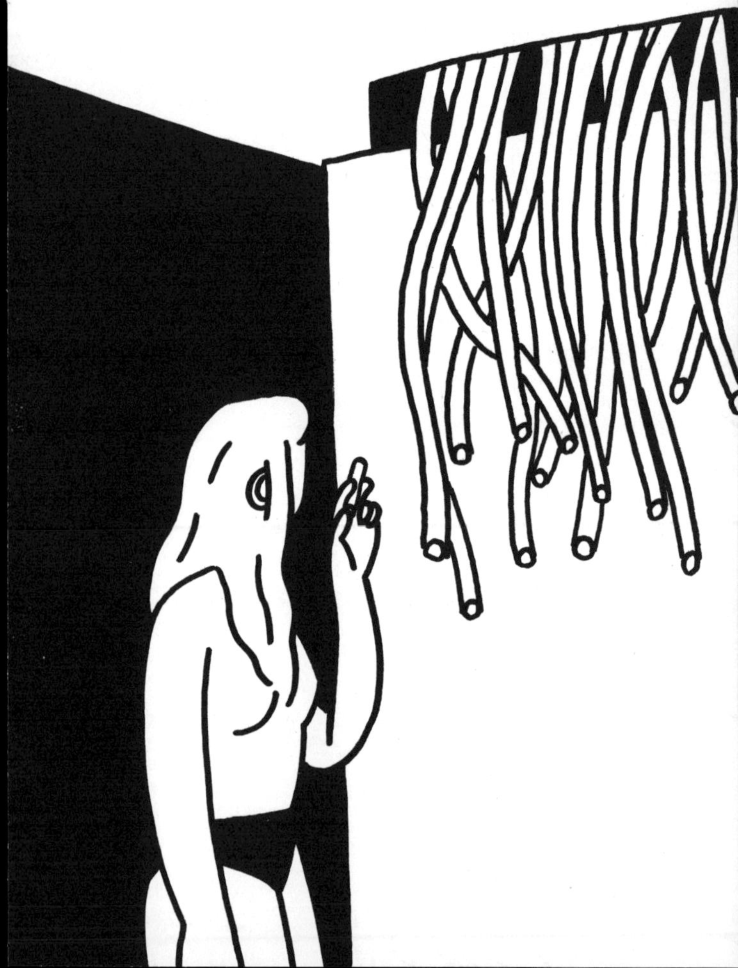

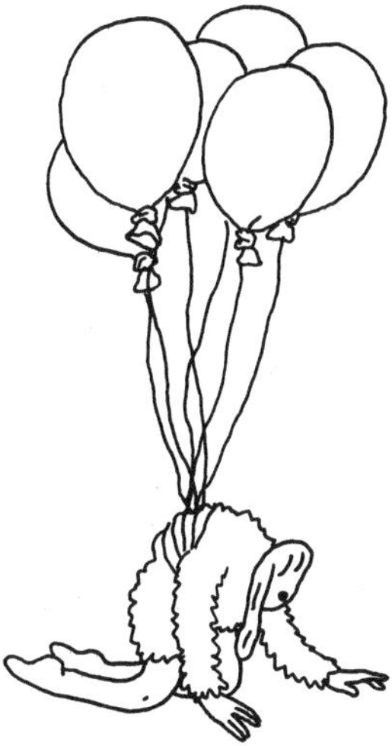

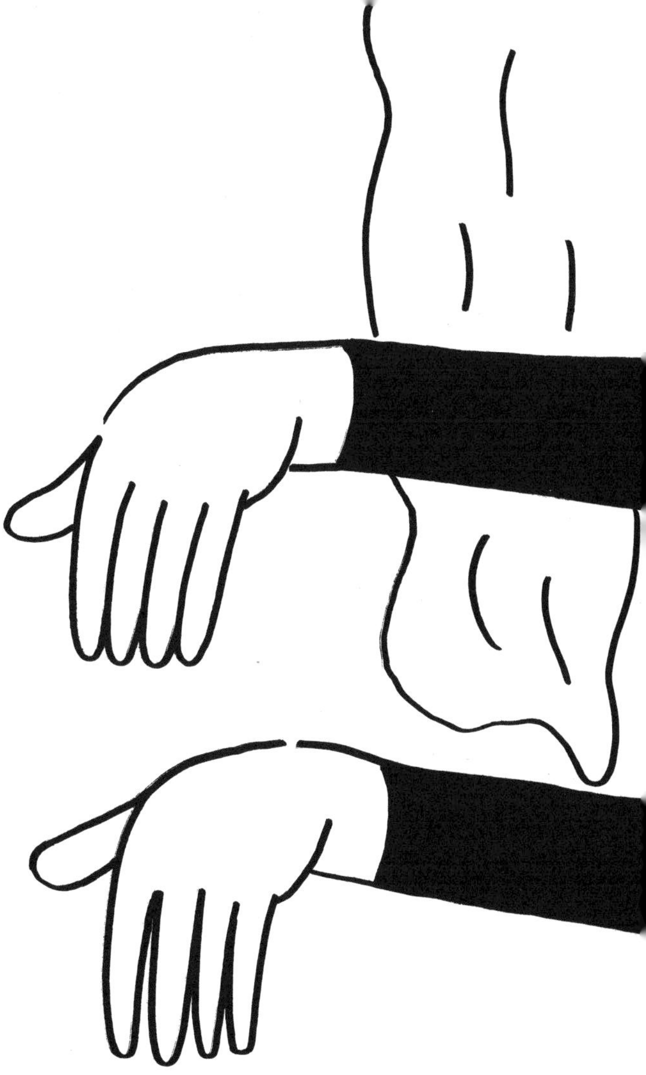

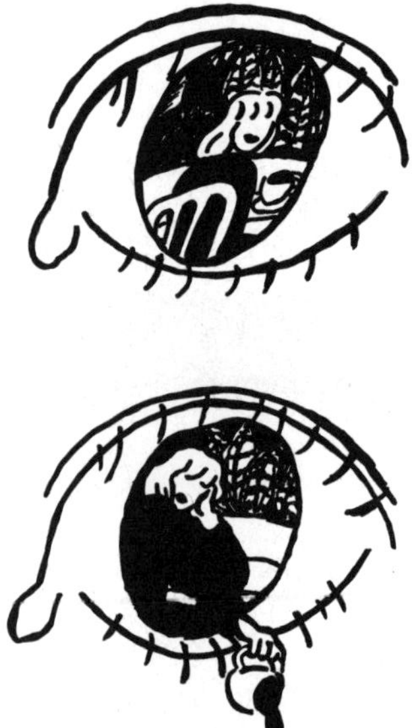

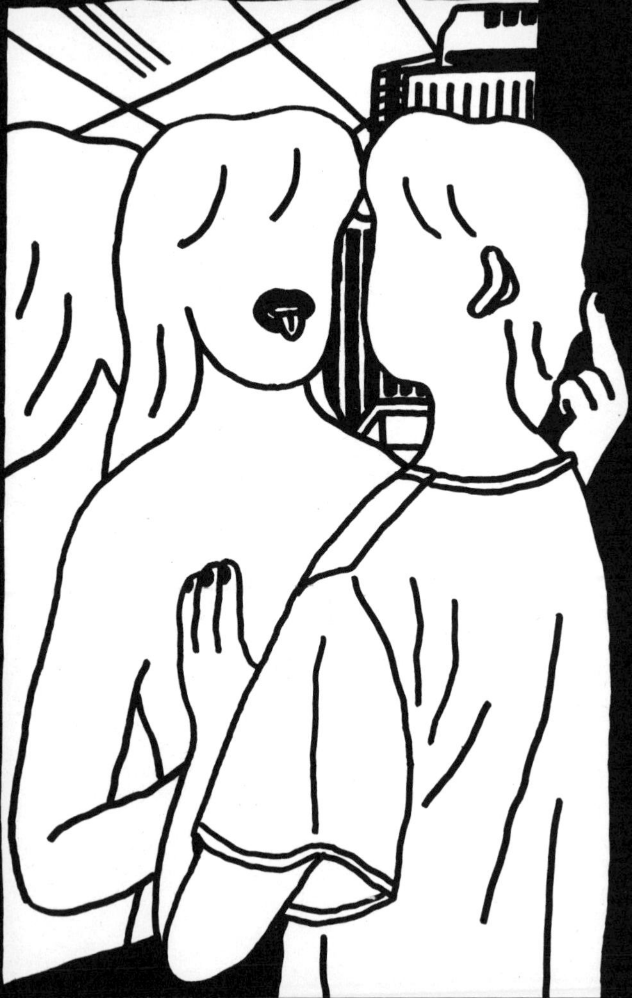

FILTERS
FILTERS

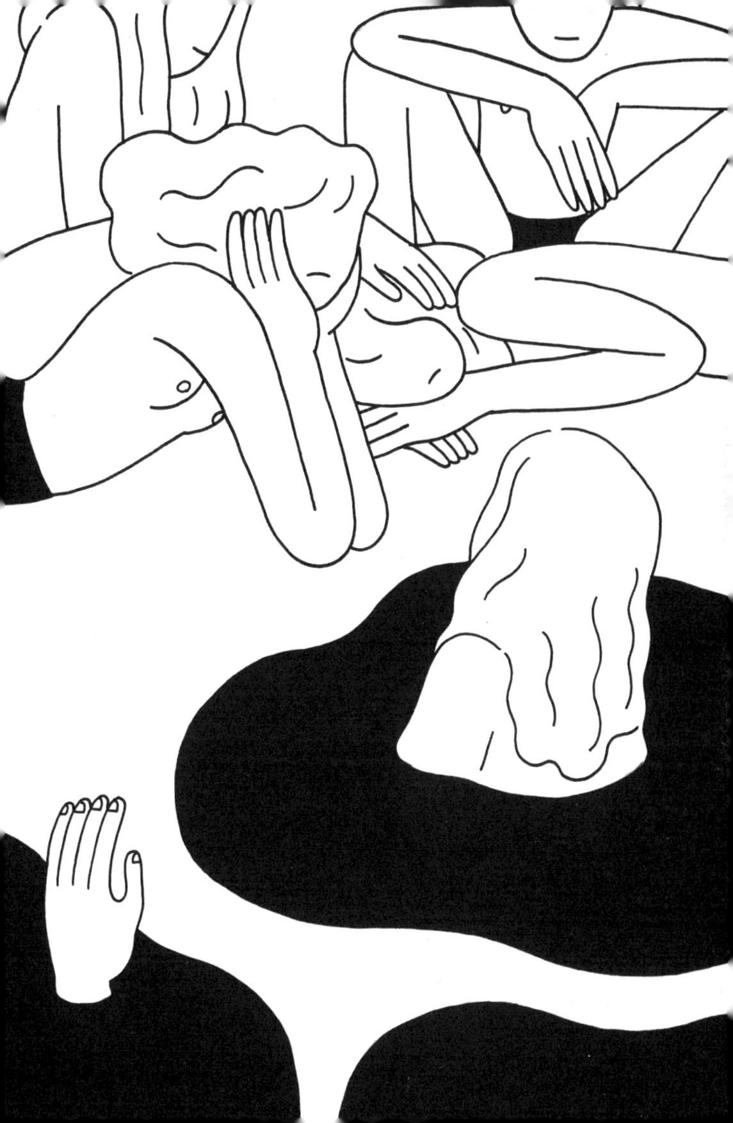